Oscar's Opposites

by Sam Godwin

Today is Oscar's birthday.

I wonder what his birthday present will be.

'Is it a **big** present or a **small** present?' Oscar asks his brother Stan.

7

'Is it a **tall** present or a **short** present?' Oscar asks his sister Suzy.

9

'Will I use my present when it's **hot** or when it's **cold**?' Oscar asks his mum.

11

'Is it a **soft** present or a **hard** present?' Oscar asks his dad.

13

'Will I use my present when it's **wet** or **dry**?' Oscar asks his cousin Molly.

'Is it a **heavy** present or a **light** present?' Oscar asks his granny.

What can the presents be?

Big

Small

Tall

Short

18

Cold

Hot

Wet

Dry

Light

Soft

Hard

Heavy

19

Happy Birthday Oscar!

21

22